DON'T EVER CHANGE, BOOPSIE

Selected cartoons from

THE PRESIDENT
IS A LOT SMARTER
THAN YOU THINK

Fawcett Popular Library Books
By G. B. Trudeau:

Doonesbury Series

☐ BRAVO FOR LIFE'S LITTLE IRONIES 08322 $1.50

☐ DON'T EVER CHANGE, BOOPSIE 00608 $1.75

☐ EVEN REVOLUTIONARIES LIKE CHOCOLATE CHIP COOKIES 00622 $1.75

☐ I HAVE NO SON 08323 $1.75

☐ JUST A FRENCH MAJOR FROM THE BRONX 00623 $1.75

☐ THE PRESIDENT IS A LOT SMARTER THAN YOU THINK 00607 $1.75

A *Doonesbury* book

Don't Ever Change, Boopsie

by G.B. Trudeau

FAWCETT POPULAR LIBRARY • NEW YORK

DON'T EVER CHANGE, BOOPSIE

The cartoons in this book have appeared in newspapers in the United States and abroad under the auspices of Universal Press Syndicate.

Published by Fawcett Popular Library, a unit of CBS Publications, the Consumer Publishing Division of CBS Inc., by arrangement with Holt, Rinehart and Winston, Inc.

ISBN: 0-445-00608-0

PRINTED IN THE UNITED STATES OF AMERICA

19 18 17 16 15 14 13 12 11

HEY, RUFUS! WHAT GIVES? YOU'RE SUPPOSED TO BE INSIDE HAVING A LESSON WITH ME!

A LESSON? YOU CRAZY, MAN? TODAY'S "AFRO-AMERICAN DAY!" A NATIONAL BLACK HOLIDAY!
G B Lindsay

OH, GEE, I'M SORRY. I DIDN'T KNOW. SEE YOU TOMORROW.

"AFRO-AMERICAN DAY?"
BEST I COULD THINK OF ON THE SPUR OF THE MOMENT...

CAMPUS NEWS. MAY I HELP YOU?... AH, YESSIR, HOW ARE YOU?.... AH, WAIT A SEC, LEMME SEE..

AH, NO, I'M SORRY. DOESN'T LOOK LIKE WE HAVE ANY ROOM. THE ISSUE IS ALREADY FILLED UP... COMPLETELY!

YES, SIR.. I'M SURE IT **IS** THE LATEST WORD, BUT WE JUST DON'T HAVE THE ROOM...

...BUT THANKS ANYWAY, MR. ELLSBERG.

TONIGHT'S COMMENT IS BY ROGER MUDD.

THANK YOU, WALTER. I DON'T HAVE MUCH TO SAY TONIGHT. AS USUAL, THE WORLD'S GOTTEN WORSE, AND I'M STUCK WITH REPORTING IT...

DO YOU THINK I ENJOY BRINGING YOU NEWS OF WAR, FAMINE, DISEASE AND TRAGEDY? DO YOU THINK I **LIKE** DEPRESSING THE ENTIRE NATION? BECAUSE I DON'T! I **HATE IT!!**

HEY, YOU! YOU WITH THE WEIRD HELMET! WHERE'D YOU COME FROM?
10
71
30
1

HOW DO, CAP'N AMERICA! MY NAME'S ZONKER! COACH SAYS THAT I'M PLAYING UPTIGHT END FOR YOU!
10
71
30
1

OL' ZONKER'S GOT THE MOST CRAZY FAR OUT HANDS IN THE COUNTY. THEY'RE JUST HEEEWACK TOOO FAR, FAR OUT!

71 30

HEY, WEIRDO! STAND FORWARD!
10
71
30
1

WELL, ZONKER, WANT TO TRY YOUR HAND AT CARRYING THE BALL?!
10
11
71
30
1

NEGATIVE, CAPTAIN AMERICA, SIRE! YOU'RE INTO A FREAKY POWER TRIP WHICH I'M HAVING A HARD TIME DIGGING..
10
18
71
30
1

WHAT'D HE JUST SAY?
"NO."
FAR OUT.
10
18
71
32
1
GBTrudeau

SNIFF
SNIFF

ZONKER! ARE YOU SMOKING THE DREADED KILLER MARIJUANA IN MY HUDDLE!?
SURE, CAP'N. WANT SOME?

ARE YOU CRAZY?! DO YOU KNOW WHAT THAT EVIL WEED LEADS TO? DO YOU?

COMMUNISM!
OH, DEAR.

DID ANYONE CATCH THE NEWS LAST NIGHT? GOVERNOR REAGAN, MY POLITICAL IDOL, WAS ON!!
10
71
30
1

WOW! TALK ABOUT VERSATILITY! THAT GUY'S AS GOOD A POLITICIAN AS HE WAS AN ACTOR!
10
71
32
1

HEH-HEH. I'LL GO ALONG WITH THAT.

YOU SAID IT, I DIDN'T.
GBTrudeau

DID YOU HEAR THAT THE COPS ARE TRYING TO INDICT CALVIN AGAIN?
WELL, HE DESERVES IT. I HOPE THEY DON'T PULL THEIR PUNCHES!

NO, "INDICT" MEANS JUST GETTING HIM INTO COURT.
WELL, I DON'T LIKE THE TRICKY WAY HIS LAWYER GOT HIM OFF THE HOOK LAST TIME.

WHAT'S WRONG WITH A FEDERAL INTERJECTION!?
HEY, WATCH YOUR LANGUAGE, FELLA!

WE DON'T COMMUNICATE SO GOOD, DO WE?
WHAT?
GBTrudeau

HI, MARK. WHO'S YOUR NEW FRIEND?
MIKE, I'D LIKE YOU TO MEET NICHOLE. SHE'S A FRESHMAN HERE THIS YEAR.

HI, NICHOLE.
NICHOLE, THIS IS MICHAEL DOONES-BURY.
HEH, HEH. **YOU'RE** MICHAEL DOONES-BURY?

AH, YUP..
HEH-HEH! HA, HA! HA!

I'VE BEEN TELLING HER ALL ABOUT YOU.
HA! HA! HA! HA! HA!

BOOPSIE, I WANTED TO HAVE THIS LITTLE DISCUSSION BECAUSE I DON'T THINK YOU UNDER-STAND HOW MIS-TREATED YOU ARE..

B.D. TREATS YOU LIKE A COMMON HOUSEHOLD OBJECT! DO YOU KNOW WHAT YOU'RE DOING? DO YOU WANT TO BE EXPLOITED?

OOH! THAT SOUNDS SEXY!! WHAT DO I HAVE TO DO TO GET "EXPLOITED"?!

C'MON! TELL ME, TELL ME! HOW DO I GET "EXPLOITED"?
GBTrudeau

WELL, DOES ANY OF WHAT I'VE SAID MAKE SENSE TO YOU?

WELL, OF COURSE. I'M NOT TOTALLY INSENSITIVE, YOU KNOW. I AGREE COMPLETELY THAT WOMEN ARE EQUAL TO MEN IN ALL RESPECTS.

NO, NO, DOONESBURY! YOU MISSED MY POINT ENTIRELY! WOMEN AREN'T EQUAL...

WE'RE BETTER.
GBTrudeau

YOU KNOW, BOOPSIE, I THINK ONE OF THE REASONS YOU'RE SO OUT OF IT IS THAT YOU'RE SO UNEDUCATED, UNREAD...

WHAT'S GOING ON HERE?
NICHOLE'S CRITICIZING ME FOR NOT READING ENOUGH.

WHAT! SHE READS PLENTY! TELL HER, BOOPSIE! TELL HER WHAT YOU READ!

I READ "VOGUE" EVERY MONTH!
SO THERE!

I HAD ANOTHER FIGHT WITH NICHOLE TODAY.
OH?

SHE WAS ACCUSING ME OF DATING A MALE CHAUVINIST SOMETHING OR ANOTHER. I TOLD HER SHE WAS CRAZY AND JUST A SILLY!

WASN'T I A GOOD GIRL?

DON'T EVER CHANGE, BOOPSIE.
O.K.
GBTrudeau

HEY, NICHOLE.
WHY SO
DEPRESSED?

OH, I DON'T KNOW... I
JUST HAD ANOTHER ONE
OF MY NON-DEBATES
WITH BOOPSIE. SHE ALWAYS
MAKES ME REALIZE
WHAT A RAW DEAL
WOMEN HAVE IN THE
WORLD.

WELL, IT JUST SEEMS THAT MEN ALWAYS HAVE BELITTLING, ULTERIOR MOTIVES.
AH, C'MON, NICHOLE. IT'S NOT THAT BAD..
SIGH .. AH, WELL, I GUESS IT'S A PROBLEM I'LL HAVE TO WORK OUT BY MYSELF..

WANNA TALK ABOUT IT OVER DINNER?

O.K., KIRBY, WHY'D YOU DROP THAT PASS?
WELL, B.D., AS I WAS LINING UP, FOR SOME REASON I BEGAN TO WONDER HOW TRICIA AND ED COX WERE DOING UP IN BOSTON.
10
81
71
30
1

I WONDERED WHAT THEIR RELATIONSHIP WAS LIKE- YOU KNOW, IF EDDIE WAS TREATING HER REAL GOOD OR NOT.. IN FACT, I GOT SO ABSORBED IN MY MUSINGS, I DIDN'T SEE THE BALL COMING..
10
81
71
30
1

I WONDER IF IT'S TOO LATE TO SWITCH TO SOCCER.

HEY, BOSS. WHAT'JA TYPING?
IT'S MY NEW WEEKLY COLUMN I'M WRITING FOR THE COLLEGE PAPER.
TAP
TAP
TAP

I'M CALLING IT "LANDSCAPES." BASICALLY, IT'S A SERIES WHICH ATTEMPTS TO CREATE SOMETHING MEANINGFUL OUT OF THE RANDOM MOMENTS OF PAIN AND PLEASURE IN MY LIFE.

TAP
TAP
TAP

DON'T FORGET THE RANDOM MOMENTS OF LUNACY.
GBTrudeau

TELL ME ABOUT THIS NEW COLUMN OF YOURS.
WELL, IT'S CALLED "LANDSCAPES." IT'S ABOUT SENSITIVITY.
TAP
TAP
TAP

I'M TRYING TO DEAL WITH FEELINGS COMMON TO ALL— LOVE, HATE, JEALOUSY, AGONY, ECSTASY, PASSION, FEAR, ANXIETY, AND, OF COURSE, ANGUISH.

YOU KNOW, MICHAEL, I'M CONSTANTLY AMAZED BY YOU.
TAP
TAP
TAP

YOU'RE A FAR BIGGER TURKEY THAN I EVER DREAMED.
GBTrudeau

ALRIGHT, BOYS, I WANT SOME GOOD BLOCKING ON THIS TOUCHDOWN PLAY...
CAP'N AMERICA, SIR?!
10
71
30

WHAT IS IT NOW, ZONKER?
WELL, CAP'N, I WAS JUST THINKING THAT IF YOU'RE ABOUT TO MAKE A BIG PLAY, YOU SHOULD ADJUST YOUR HELMET.
10
71
30

YOU SEE, A REAL SUPERSTAR TILTS HIS HELMET A LITTLE MORE FORWARD. IT SHADES HIS EYES AND MAKES HIM A MYSTERIOUS DUDE... HERE, LET ME HELP, CAP'N!
10
71
30

PLAY BALL!
©GBTrudeau
10
71
30
1

ZONKER!
SIRE?

ZONKER, I WOULD LIKE TO ASK YOU A SERIOUS QUESTION. IF YOU HATE PRACTICE SO MUCH, WHY DID YOU BOTHER TO COME OUT FOR FOOTBALL IN THE FIRST PLACE?

BECAUSE, CAPTAIN AMERICA, I ADMIRE YOU! YES! ADMIRE YOU! ADMIRE AND RESPECT YOU!
10
71
30

HEH, HEH! HEH!
GBTrudeau
71
30

JONATHON, I'M GOING TO THROW A LONG BOMB TO YOU. BUTTON HOOK ON THE 30. GOT IT?
O.K., B.D.!
10
71
30

HOLD IT, CAP'N!
10
71
30

IF MY ONLY CAPTAIN IS GOING TO THROW INTO THE SUN, THEN HE'LL BE NEEDING SOME EYE BLACK TO CUT DOWN THE GLARE!
10
71
30

I DON'T KNOW HOW MUCH MORE OF THIS ABUSE I CAN TAKE.
FAR OUT. HEH-HEH.
10
71
30

SMACK
GOOD LUCK, TIGER!

SMACK
GOOD LUCK, TIGER!

THAT DOES IT!!
YEECH! CHAPPED LIPS!

ZONKER, EVER SINCE YOU JOINED THE TEAM, YOU'VE BEEN A PAIN, A NUISANCE, AND A GENERAL TROUBLE MAKER!
10
11
71
30

SNIFF
SNIFF
10
11
71

WAAH!!

NOW LOOK WHAT YOU'VE DONE, YOU BULLY!
HE DIDN'T MEAN IT, ZONKER.
SOB! SOB! SNIFF
POOR GUY!

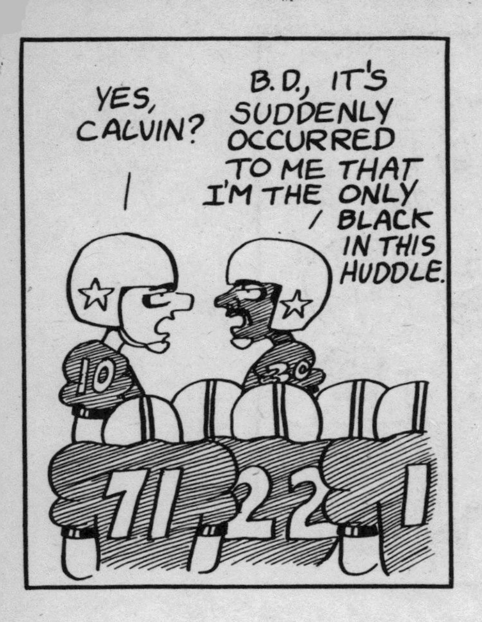
YES, CALVIN?
B.D., IT'S SUDDENLY OCCURRED TO ME THAT I'M THE ONLY BLACK IN THIS HUDDLE.
10
30
71
22
1

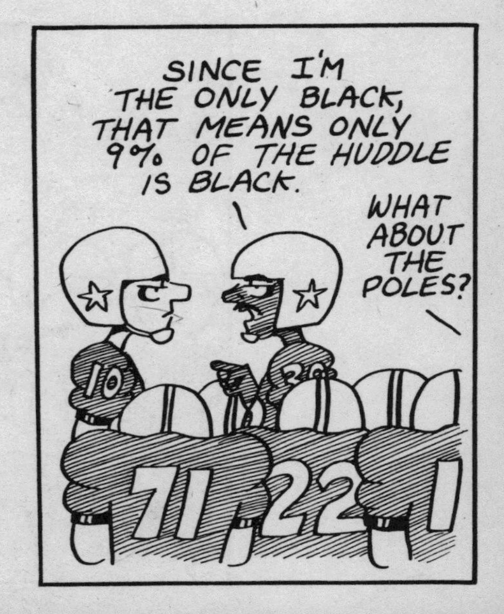
SINCE I'M THE ONLY BLACK, THAT MEANS ONLY 9% OF THE HUDDLE IS BLACK.
WHAT ABOUT THE POLES?
10
30
71
22
1

I'M THE ONLY POLE IN THIS HUDDLE! BLATANT DISCRIMINATION!

MORE BLACKS!
MORE POLES!
MORE FREAKS!

HEY, B.D.! JOHN KERRY OF THE VIETNAM VETS IS SPEAKING AT THE AUDITORIUM! WANNA GO?
YOU BETTER!

IF YOU CARE ABOUT THIS COUNTRY AT ALL, YOU BETTER GO LISTEN TO THAT JOHN KERRY FELLOW...

HE SPEAKS WITH A RARE ELOQUENCE AND ASTONISHING CONVICTION. IF YOU SEE NO ONE ELSE THIS YEAR, YOU MUST SEE JOHN KERRY!

WHO WAS THAT?
JOHN KERRY.
©GBTrudeau

I THINK IT'S BECOME CLEAR TO MOST OF US THAT THIS WAR IS A HIDEOUS MISTAKE!

YET EVEN WITH THE REVELATIONS OF THE VIETNAM PAPERS, THE PRESIDENT REFUSES TO CHANGE HIS POLICY.

AS FAR AS THE PRESIDENT'S CONCERNED, VIETNAM MEANS NOT HAVING TO SAY YOU'RE SORRY!!
GBTrudeau

YOU'RE REALLY CLICKING TONIGHT, YOU GORGEOUS PREPPIE.
YEA!
YEA!
CLAP!
RIGHT ON!
CLAP!

MY FRIENDS, THIS WAR HAS COST US BILLIONS OF DOLLARS AND THOUSANDS OF LIVES! WASTED! ALL WASTED!

YOU FLAMING HYPOCRITE!

HOW CAN YOU MORALIZE AFTER THROWING ALL YOUR MEDALS ON THE CAPITOL STEPS LAST SPRING!

DO YOU HAVE ANY IDEA HOW MUCH THOSE MEDALS COST THE GOVERNMENT?

HEY! HOW ABOUT A LITTLE SERVICE HERE?

GEE, I'M SORRY— I DIDN'T HEAR YOU COME IN. I WAS SO ABSORBED IN "LYSISTRATA," ARISTOPHANES'S GREAT MASTERPIECE, YOU KNOW?

"SUCH UNCOMPROMISING SATIRE, WRITTEN WITH RECKLESS HIGH SPIRITS! THE AUTHOR HAS AN UNERRING EYE FOR WHAT IS POMPOUS, SENTENTIOUS AND FOOLISH ABOUT SOCIETY." HOW I HATE TO TEAR MYSELF AWAY!

BOY, AM I GOING TO FEEL SILLY ASKING FOR A GRILLED CHEESE SANDWICH.

SAY, CALVIN, IF YOU COULD HAVE YOUR CHOICE, WOULD YOU RATHER BE BLACK OR WHITE?

GEE, I'M NOT SURE. I KNOW I WOULDN'T WANT TO BE WHITE... ON THE OTHER HAND, BEING BLACK IS NO BARREL OF LAUGHS.

I SUPPOSE I COULD COMPROMISE.. YOU KNOW, BE A PUERTO RICAN OR AN INDIAN.. GEEZ, I DON'T KNOW...

ACTUALLY, MIKE, IT'S A PRETTY STUPID QUESTION.
GBTrudeau

SAY, RUFUS, IF YOU COULD HAVE YOUR CHOICE, WOULD YOU RATHER BE BLACK OR WHITE?

MIKE, THAT'S A REALLY STUPID QUESTION.
THAT'S WHAT CALVIN TOLD ME YESTERDAY. BUT WHAT WOULD YOUR ANSWER BE ANYWAY?

WELL.. I'M PRETTY SURE I WOULDN'T LIKE BEING WHITE.
WHY?

I'D BE FORCED TO PUT UP WITH THEM UPPITY BLACK FOLK.
GBTrudeau

HI YA, CAL. WHAT CAN I DO FOR YOU?

YOU GUYS WANT TO MAKE A DONATION TO THE PANTHER DEFENSE FUND?
SORRY, CAL, I'M A LITTLE LOW ON CASH..
ME, TOO.

I DON'T LIKE THE LOOKS OF THIS.

WE INTERRUPT THIS PROGRAM TO BRING YOU A SPECIAL MESSAGE FROM THE WHITE HOUSE...

GOOD EVENING, MY FELLOW AMERICANS. I JUST WANTED TO TELL YOU THAT I HOPED YOU WERE ALL ENJOYING MY 90 DAY FREEZE.

LOWER TAXES, NO PRICE INCREASES— PRETTY GREAT, HUH?.. SO NEXT YEAR, WHEN YOU'RE THINKING ABOUT THE CANDIDATES, LOOK AT MY RECORD, O.K.?.. WILL YOU DO THAT FOR ME?.. FINE!

HEY, BACK THERE! HOW ABOUT SOME COFFEE?

PLEASE EXCUSE ME, SIR! I WAS VERY INVOLVED IN ANDRÉ MALRAUX'S TEMPESTUOUS "MAN'S FATE." IT'S VERY HARD TO PUT DOWN.

MALRAUX? WOW! LAST TIME IT WAS ARISTOPHANES.. SOME WAITRESS... SAY, WHAT'S YOUR NAME, LUV?
ANASTASIA.

"ANASTASIA"?
IS THE MOCHA TOO TART, SIR?
©GBTrudeau

B.D., I COULDN'T HELP NOTICING THAT YOU STILL HAVE TAKEN NO ACTION IN BRING-ING RACIAL BALANCE TO THIS HUDDLE!

LISTEN, CALVIN, I'M GETTING TIRED OF YOUR WHINING! I DON'T WANT TO HEAR ANOTHER PEEP OUT OF YOU UNTIL THE SEASON'S OVER!

WHAT! UNTIL THE SEASON'S OVER?! WHAT IS THIS, A 90 DAY FREEZE ON CIVIL RIGHTS?! HUH? HUH?
10
30
71
22
1

YOU CAN'T DEVALUATE THE BLACK!!
10
71
22
1
©BTrudeau

WOW, MIKE, WE'RE VERY LUCKY TO GET INTO PROFESSOR CHARLIE GREEN'S COURSE. THEY SAY IT'S JUST ABOUT THE MOST BEAUTIFUL COURSE AROUND..

BE FREE AND FREAKY, AND DON'T GET INTO AN ANXIETY BAG. STAY OR LEAVE – DO WHAT COMES THE MOST NATURALLY FOR YOU. CLASS DISMISSED.

THEY ALSO SAY IT'S A LITTLE UNSTRUCTURED.

MY FRIENDS, THERE IS LITTLE IN THE **CONSCIOUSNESS II** MENTALITY WHICH I FIND ALLURING!

IT IS BASED ON A FALSE LOVE OF ACHIEVEMENT, OF WANTING TO APPEAR SUCCESSFUL IN ONE'S NEIGHBORS' EYES!

SUCCESS, GLORY, GRATIFICATION AND HERO-WORSHIP ARE THE BARBARIC REMNANTS OF AN ARCHAIC SOCIETY!!
GBTrudeau

HEAVY!
WOW!
CLAP! CLAP!
YEA!
CLAP! CLAP!
OH, WOW!

LOOK! THERE'S CHARLIE GREEN, THE SIDEWALK GURU. LET'S GO RAP WITH HIM!

SAY PROFESSOR GREEN, I'D LIKE TO ASK YOU A QUESTION. WHAT DO YOU SAY TO THE MANY CYNICS WHO PUT DOWN YOUR BEST-SELLING BOOK?

A CYNIC IS SOMEONE WHO KNOWS THE PRICE OF EVERYTHING AND THE VALUE OF NOTHING.

BEAUTIFUL!
OH, WOW!
PRETTY SOON I'M GOING TO HAVE TO START CHARGING.
WOW!
HEAVY!
© G.B. Trudeau

..OOH! AREN'T YOU PROFESSOR GREEN?!

I'VE BEEN DYING TO MEET YOU!! I **LOVED** YOUR CUTE BOOK!

EVERYONE LOVES IT! DO YOU KNOW WHERE YOUR DARLING BOOK IS ALWAYS A BIG HIT?!.

COCKTAIL PARTIES!
GBTrudeau

I'VE GOT TO HAND IT TO YOU, PROFESSOR GREEN, YOU'VE HANDLED YOUR NEW-FOUND FAME WITH REAL DIGNITY.

YOU'VE SHUNNED PUBLICITY, AND YOU HAVEN'T EVEN GONE ON THE "TONIGHT SHOW."
OF COURSE NOT..

..I PREACH THE REJECTION OF ALL THE STANDARD MEASURES OF SUCCESS. FOR ME TO GO ON THE "TONIGHT SHOW" WOULD BE INCONSISTENT!

ALSO, I WASN'T ASKED.
GBTrudeau

AMAZING!..

... HE'S GOT HIS OWN APOSTLES NOW.
GBTrudeau

PROFESSOR GREEN, THERE HAVE BEEN MORE COMPLAINTS FROM YOUR COLLEAGUES ABOUT YOUR CLASSROOM ANTICS!
OH.

GREEN, AREN'T YOU CONCERNED AT ALL ABOUT YOUR CAREER? YOUR TENURE?
'TIS FAR BETTER TO BE LOVED THAN TENURED! HEH-HEH.

GREEN! ARE YOU STONED?
ALL TOGETHER NOW, CHILDREN! CONSONANT I, CONSUMMÉ II, RESUMÉ IV, WOW!

SHAPE UP, MAN!
WHY? I'M BEAUTIFUL THE WAY I AM.

WHAT'S THIS? TWO DOLLARS FOR A COKE?!

SORRY, KID, BUT THE 90-DAY FREEZE IS ENDING AND PRICES ARE GOING UP.

BUT $2.00 FOR A COKE. YOU CAN'T DO THAT!
LISSEN, KID, DON'T TELL ME WHAT I CAN AND CANNOT DO!!

I'VE GOT THREE MONTHS OF INFLATION TO CATCH UP ON!

PRESIDENT KING! DO YOU HAVE ANY IDEA HOW LONG I WAITED OUTSIDE?!
SORRY, MARK. WHAT CAN I DO FOR YOU?

I'VE COME TO TAKE OVER YOUR OFFICE! WILL YOU GO PEACEFULLY?
TAKE OVER MY OFFICE?! THAT'S SO CORNY, IT'S UNBELIEVABLE.

I EXPECTED BETTER THINGS FROM YOU, MARK! "TAKING OVER OFFICES" WENT OUT IN '69 AFTER THE HARVARD INCIDENT! YOUR METHODS ARE UNBELIEVABLY TRITE!

DO YOU HEAR ME? TRITE, TRITE, TRITE!!

POOF!

DARNNIT, BERNIE! DO YOU HAVE TO TEST YOUR INANE WEREWOLF FORMULA WHILE I'M WORKING? YOU KEEP SHEDDING ALL OVER MY EXPERIMENTS!
O.K., O.K.! I'LL TAKE SOMETHING ELSE.

THANK YOU.
DON'T MENTION IT.
GBTrudeau

MIKE, I'D LIKE YOU TO MEET WALTER, THE DELEGATE FROM C.I.T.– HE'LL BE STAYING WITH YOU FOR THE DURATION OF THE STUDENT CONGRESS.

SO YOU'RE FROM THE CONNECTICUT INSTITUTE OF TECHNOLOGY, EH, WALTER? WELL, I DON'T KNOW MUCH ABOUT SCIENCE, BUT I'M CERTAINLY EAGER TO EXCHANGE IDEAS ON OTHER SUBJECTS.

BLEEP.

I WAS AFRAID OF THIS.
NULL SET. ROGER. BLEEP! BLEEP!
GBTrudeau

WELCOME, DELEGATES, TO OUR FALL STUDENT CONGRESS. I'M VERY HAPPY THAT SO MANY OF YOU COULD MAKE IT.

TO START THE PROCEEDINGS OFF, WE'D LIKE TO SHOW YOU A FILM CLIP ON GOVERNMENT ATROCITIES, SUCH AS VIETNAM, WIRE TAPPINGS, AND REPRESSION.
O.K., ROLL IT!

RRRR
WILL YA LOOK AT THAT!
RRR

STRIKE!!
STRIKE!
STRING.
GOVERNMENT ATROCITIES ALWAYS BRING US YOUTHS TOGETHER.
GBTrudeau

MIKE, HOW'S THAT SCIENCE FREAK WALTER DOING?
O.K., I GUESS. WE DON'T HAVE MUCH IN COMMON, SO I BROUGHT BERNIE OVER TO TALK WITH HIM.

HEY, BERNIE! HOW ARE YOU AND WALTER GETTING ALONG?

JUST FINE, MIKE!

..WE'VE BEEN TALKING SHOP!

I'D LIKE TO START OFF THIS SECOND SESSION OF THE CONGRESS BY ASKING EACH OF YOU TO STATE YOUR PARTICULAR DEMANDS AT THIS TIME. .... O.K., **HARVARD!**

END THE WAR!

OH. YES, THAT'S A GOOD ONE. NICE THINKING, STANFORD. ..UM.. NOTRE DAME!

MORE FOOTBALL GAMES!
GBTrudeau

SAY, MARK, IS THE CONGRESS PROGRESSING WELL?
SURE! TODAY WE HAD A VERY EXCITING VOTE!..

THE CONGRESS WAS DEADLOCKED ON THIS PARTICULAR RESOLUTION... THEN, SUDDENLY A RUMOR BROKE THAT THE DELEGATE FROM MICHIGAN STATE HAD BEEN DATING THE DELEGATE FROM VASSAR. THIS MIGHT HAVE PREJUDICED MICHIGAN'S VOTE.

FINALLY, THE VASSAR DELEGATE BROKE DOWN AND CONFESSED, AND BOTH WERE DISQUALIFIED. THIS DISPLAY SO MOVED THE SMITH DELEGATE THAT SHE IN TURN SWITCHED HER VOTE, AND THE AYES HAD. IT! WOW, TALK ABOUT EXCITEMENT!

FELLOW DELEGATES, RACISM MUST BE FOUGHT AND IT MUST BE FOUGHT ON A GRASS ROOTS LEVEL!
YEAH!
RIGHT ON!
YES!

..BUT I DIDN'T COME ALL THE WAY HERE FROM HOWARD UNIVERSITY JUST TO TALK! I WANT TO SEE ACTION!
YEAH!
YEA!
RIGHT ON!

ALRIGHT, YOU CATS! SINGLE FILE, EVERYONE TO THE GHETTO!
YEA! YEA! YEA!

YOU'VE GOT NICE CROWD CONTROL, FELLAH!
RIGHT ON!

HOW'D THE CONGRESS GO TODAY?
NOT SO WELL. THE DELEGATE FROM N.Y.U. INTRODUCED SOME GREAT RESOLUTIONS ON VIETNAM, BUT THE CONSERVATIVE DELEGATES KEPT VOTING THEM DOWN.

INITIALLY, IT WAS RESOLVED THAT WE RECOMMENDED IMMEDIATE WITHDRAWAL. THEN IT GOT DOWN TO THE OL' SETTING A DATE BUSINESS. THEN IT BECAME RESOLVED THAT WE JUST DISAPPROVED OF THE WAR... IT BECAME VAGUER AND VAGUER.

WHAT'D YOU FINALLY RESOLVE?

"WAR IS BAD."

HEY!
OFF THE WAR!
HEY!
NO, OFF THE PIGS!
NO, END THE POLITICAL MACHINE!
SHUT UP..
NO!

BROTHERS! SISTERS! PEACE! YOU MUST STAND TOGETHER! YOU MUST HAVE A COMMON GOAL!

KILL THE MODERATOR!
GBTrudeau

KILL THE MODERATOR!..
THAT'S NOT EXACTLY WHAT I HAD IN MIND..
SPLAT!

FELLOW DELEGATES, WELCOME TO THE FINAL BANQUET OF THE FALL STUDENT CONGRESS. HERE TO READ AN ORIGINAL AFTER-DINNER POEM FOR US IS WILLY LEAWOOD OF TUFTS.

FASCISM DOTH PROVOKE THE IRE, WE SINK INTO THE FILTH AND MIRE!

AGONY DOES IMPEND, DEATH WILL NOT AMEND! AIEE!
©BTrudeau

YOU'RE A LITTLE UPTIGHT, AREN'T YOU, WILLY?
CLAP!
CLAP!
CLAP!
CLAP!
CLAP!
CLAP!
CLAP!

HEY, MIKE, DO YOU AND B.D. WANT TO GO TO A MOVIE TONIGHT?

HEY, B.D., WANT TO GO TO A FLICK TONIGHT?
SORRY! I'M READING.

READING? WHAT ARE YOU READING?
"LOVE STORY," "WAR AND PEACE," "CRIME IN AMERICA," "ZELDA," AND "DELIVERANCE."

HIS COPY OF READER'S DIGEST MUST HAVE ARRIVED THIS MORNING...
GBTrudeau

HEY! IS IT SNOWING OUT?!
SURE. IT HAS BEEN FOR TWO HOURS!

FAR OUT!
HEY, WAIT!

DOONESBURY! DO YOU KNOW WHAT THIS STUFF IS?! IT'S SNOW, MAN, ACTUAL BONA-FIDE SNOW!

YIPPIE!
YOU'RE EASY TO PLEASE...
GBTrudeau

ZONKER?
YEAH?
71
30
18
10

ZONKER, MY MAN, THIS IS IT... WE ONLY HAVE TIME FOR THIS ONE LAST PLAY – A LONG BOMB TO YOU! IF YOU MISS IT, WE LOSE THE GAME AND THE CHAMPIONSHIP. IT'S UP TO YOU, ZONKER...
10
71
30
18

GEE, I'M SORRY TO HEAR THAT, CAP'N! I DIDN'T THINK YOU'D EVER CALL ON ME, SO I JUST KNOCKED OFF A DELIGHTFUL BOTTLE OF ROSÉ.
HIC
10
71
3
18

AIEEE!
OH, WOW! GOLD FILLINGS!
10
71
3
18
©B. Trudeau

HEY, ZONKER, IS THAT YOU?
SSSHH! NOT SO LOUD...

HEY, WHAT ARE YOU DOING DOWN THERE?
HIDING! FROM B.D.! HE'S LOOKING FOR ME. HE WANTS TO KILL ME FOR LOSING THE BIG GAME...

WELL, ZONK, I'M ON MY WAY TO A CHRISTMAS PARTY. WANNA COME?
SORRY. CAN'T. YOU GO ON WITHOUT ME...

WE HUNTED ANIMALS HAVE NO TIME FOR LEVITY...
GBTrudeau

THANKS FOR HELPING ME WITH MY BAGS, MARK...
NO PROBLEM, ZONKER.

MY PARENTS SHOULD BE HERE ANY MINUTE...
SAY, THAT REMINDS ME— ABOUT YOUR PARENTS, ZONKER...

YEAH?
DON'T THEY RIDE YOU A LOT ABOUT YOUR HAIR AND ABOUT BLOWIN' GRASS? HOW DO YOU KEEP FROM GOING AT EACH OTHERS' THROATS?
©GBTrudeau

OH, WE MANAGE.
BABY BUMP-KINS!
HEY, MAN, QUE PASSA?

HEY! OL' MAN WEATHER! YOU CALL THIS SNOW?!

HEY, MAN! ARE THESE ITTY-BITTY SNOWFLAKES THE BEST YOU CAN DO? HUH, MAN?

BOINK!

YOU'RE A FUNNY GUY, OL' MAN WEATHER!
©B Trudeau

HI, DAD.

WHY, HELLO, SON? HOW LONG HAVE YOU BEEN HOME?
THREE DAYS.

ARE YOU ENJOYING YOUR VACATION? ARE YOU IN GOOD HEALTH? ARE YOU HAVING ANY PROBLEMS AT SCHOOL?
YES, YES, AND NO.

NICE TO HAVE YOU HOME, SON.
RIGHT.
GBTrudeau

DAD, WHAT DO YOU THINK ABOUT ATTICA?
I THINK ROCKY DID THE RIGHT THING...

AFTER ALL, WHAT WOULD YOU HAVE HIM DO — GIVE IN TO THAT RIDICULOUS DEMAND OF SAFE PASSAGE TO A NON-IMPERIALIST COUNTRY?

THINK ABOUT IT, SON! WHAT DO YOU THINK WOULD HAVE HAPPENED TO OUR RELATIONS WITH THE RUSSIANS IF THEY LEARNED WE WERE PLANNING TO PARACHUTE 750 HARDENED CRIMINALS INTO DOWNTOWN STALINGRAD?!

GOOD POINT, DAD.
DARN RIGHT!
©GBTrudeau

MARK! WILL YA HURRY UP! WE'LL BE LATE FOR YOUR GRANDMOTHER'S DINNER!
YEAH, YEAH!

WILL YOU LISTEN TO THAT! SOMETIMES I THINK THAT BOY ONLY COMES HOME JUST TO BAIT ME!

OH, C'MON DEAR! WHAT MAKES YOU SAY THAT?
OH, I DUNNO...
GBTrudeau

... CALL IT A HUNCH

MIKE? HIYA, MAN. THIS IS RUFUS!... MERRY CHRISTMAS, YOU OL' COWBOY!

HOW'VE YA BEEN?... ME?... FINE, JUST FINE. MY CHRISTMAS HAS BEEN GREAT! GOT THE TREE DECORATED UP, AND I OPENED MY PRESENT FROM MOM.

IT WAS A PENCIL ... YUP, A PENCIL! A REAL BEAUT! IT'S A NO. 3 ORANGE. IT WAS MY ONLY PRESENT, BUT I'M NOT COMPLAINING, NOT ME! I CAN'T WAIT TO TRY IT OUT! ... WELL, BYE, MIKE ... I HOPE YOU ENJOY THE REST OF YOUR CHRISTMAS!